DIFFERENTIAL CLOZE

ACTIVITIES TO DEVELOP READING COMPREHENSION

ad an ___incredible___

ut ___ancient___ (2) Egypt in school and we w

at it would be like to have lived there. We must have powerful

because ___suddenly___ (3) we found ourselves standing

banks of the ___Nile___ (4) River.

g us were crops of wheat and ___barley___ 5). An ingenious

ystem of canals carried ___water___ (6) from the Nile to the

was so hot that it was hard to ima__ne how ___anything___ (7)

w.

n wore white ___ski___ ___women___ (9) long,

white dresses. Some pe__ __re sa__ __e-up and headresses. We

ht they must be ___ric___ __hings other than food. We ___traded___ (11)

t in class that the Egyptia__ __orked ___hard___ (12) yet lo

ss items for those they __he work was done, many of the

eople didn't seem to ___ay. __ (13) or sai__ their boats whic

__ke the peop__ to ___f__ ___think___ (14) of our own

down to th__

__e made __rus reeds.

made us

Written by Lyn Couling-Brown
Published by Prim-Ed Publishing

Foreword

Differentiated Cloze is a series of three books that applies the effective and commonly used cloze techniques to assist in the development of reading and comprehension skills.

The topics chosen for the cloze text contain a variety of fiction and non-fiction material.

Two formats are used in presenting each topic to provide the pupils with different approaches to using the cloze technique and to gain maximum benefit from each lesson.

1. On the first page of each topic the missing words are provided at the bottom of each page.

2. The second page of each topic has different words missing from the text. The answers are not provided to encourage pupils to rely on context clues only.

Teachers may treat each topic with the whole class, in small groups or individually.

Both formats can be given to the children to complete, with a lengthy interval between each.

Teachers may also take into account the ability level of each pupil; giving cloze set one to the pupils needing more guidance and cloze set two to the more able pupils.

Answers for both formats are provided.

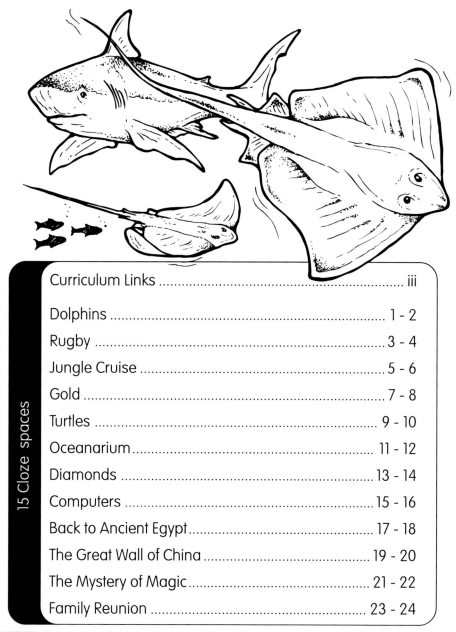

15 Cloze spaces

Differentiated Cloze Curriculum Links

The activities within the three-book series Differentiated Cloze have been written to assist the development of reading and comprehension skills. The fiction and non-fiction cloze activities encourage pupils to use a range of strategies to make sense of what they read, thus helping to develop their ability to read with fluency, accuracy, understanding and enjoyment.

The activities in Differentiated Cloze demonstrate the following objectives of the Reading Programme of Study of the English National Curriculum.

Book	Key Stage	Programme of Study		
Lower	One	Reading	Pupils should be taught:	
			1. k	to work out the sense of a sentence by rereading or reading ahead
			1.1	to focus on meaning derived from text
			5	the knowledge, skills and understanding through a range of fiction and non-fiction texts
Middle	Two	Reading	Pupils should be taught:	
			1.c	to use knowledge of grammatical structures
			1.d	to use contextual understanding
			7	the knowledge, skills and understanding through a range of fiction and non-fiction texts
Upper	Two	Reading	Pupils should be taught:	
			1.c	to use knowledge of grammatical structures
			1.d	to use contextual understanding
			7	the knowledge, skills and understanding through a range of fiction and non-fiction texts

Dolphins

Have you ever been out on a boat and seen dolphins swimming in the bow _____ (1)? It is a wonderful experience. Dolphins are _____ (2) creatures that swim in schools or pods. They show great friendliness toward _____ (3) and often swim and play around them.

A dolphin is recognised by its torpedo-shaped _____ (4) and beak-like snout. Dolphins are actually the _____ (5) whales. They have conical teeth and their flippers and _____ (6) fin usually curve to a point. Powerful tail fins propel a dolphin through the water. Their skin is _____ (7) and rubbery. A layer of fat beneath the skin keeps them _____ (8) and acts as a storage space for food.

Dolphins are very intelligent and can be _____ (9) to respond to commands in captivity. They communicate with _____ (10) other through a series of whistles, chirps, clicks and _____ (11).

Although _____ (12) have been admired by humans throughout the centuries, they have also been hunted for their rich meat and _____ (13). Many dolphins drown in fishing nets intended for fish, particularly tuna.

_____ (14) are trying to protect dolphins so they can continue to survive and we can _____ (15) these graceful and playful creatures of our seas.

observe	dolphins	body	smallest	wave
people	dorsal	moans	Conservationists	trained
oil	each	smooth	warm	sociable

Dolphins

Have you ever been out on a _____ [1] and seen dolphins swimming in the bow wave? It is a wonderful experience. Dolphins _____ [2] sociable creatures that swim in schools or pods. They show great friendliness toward people and often swim and play _____ [3] them.

A dolphin is recognised by _____ [4] torpedo-shaped body and beak-like snout. Dolphins are actually the smallest whales. They _____ [5] conical teeth and their flippers and dorsal fin usually curve to _____ [6] point. Powerful tail fins propel a dolphin through the _____ [7]. Their skin is smooth and rubbery. A layer of fat beneath the skin _____ [8] them warm and acts as a storage space for food.

_____ [9] are very intelligent and can be trained to respond to commands _____ [10] captivity. They communicate with each other through a series _____ [11] whistles, chirps, clicks and moans.

Although dolphins have been admired by humans throughout the centuries, they have also been hunted _____ [12] their rich meat and oil. Many dolphins drown in fishing nets intended for _____ [13], particularly tuna.

Conservationists are trying _____ [14] protect dolphins so they can continue to survive and we can observe these graceful _____ [15] playful creatures of our seas.

Rugby

Rugby is a popular _____ (1) sport played in many countries throughout the world. It originated in Great _____ (2) in the 1800s. It is a fast, contact sport played by two teams, each with _____ (3) players.

Each team is divided into _____ (4) forwards and seven backs. Every position has a name and _____ (5) tasks to perform.

The object of the game is to _____ (6), run with, pass and kick an oval-shaped ball to the team's goal end of a 100-_____ (7) field and place it across a try line. To _____ (8) the game, one team must score more points than the other. Points are scored for a try, a _____ (9) goal, a drop goal and a goal conversion. A goal conversion can only be taken when a _____ (10) has been scored.

It is quite difficult to score a try, because the opposition is allowed to _____ (11) the ball carrier and take possession of the ball.

If you are fortunate enough to play rugby for your _____ (12), you have the opportunity to travel around the world, wear a special _____ (13) and play rugby in front of huge crowds.

Australia's _____ (14) team is called the Wallabies, the British team is the Lions, New Zealand's team is the All Blacks and the South _____ (15) team is called the Springboks.

specific	country	African	national	team
fifteen	eight	try	penalty	uniform
tackle	Britain	metre	chase	win

Rugby

Rugby is a popular team sport played in many countries throughout the _____ (1). It originated in Great Britain in the 1800s. It is a fast, contact _____ (2) played by two teams, each _____ (3) fifteen players.

Each _____ (4) is divided into eight forwards and seven backs. Every position _____ (5) a name and specific tasks to perform.

The object _____ (6) the game is to chase, run with, pass and kick an oval-shaped _____ (7) to the team's goal end of a 100-metre field and place it _____ (8) a try line. To win the _____ (9), one team must score more points than the other. Points are scored for a try, a penalty goal, a drop goal _____ (10) a goal conversion. A goal conversion can only be taken when a try has been scored.

It is quite difficult to score a try, because the opposition is _____ (11) to tackle the ball carrier and take possession of the ball.

If you are fortunate enough to play _____ (12) for your country, you have the opportunity to travel around the world, _____ (13) a special uniform and play rugby in front of huge crowds.

Australia's national team is _____ (14) the Wallabies, the British team is the Lions, _____ (15) Zealand's team is the All Blacks and the South African team is called the Springboks.

Jungle Cruise

A trip to _____ (1) would not be complete without a visit to Disneyland! My family were awake bright and early on the day we had _____ (2) our visit.

After _____ (3) we caught the courtesy bus to Disneyland. We alighted from the bus and _____ (4) towards the huge gates. There were already several hundred people queuing. As Dad had bought our day passes earlier in the week, we were able to go through the _____ (5) gate.

'Adventureland' was our _____ (6) choice. Wandering slowly through the entrance we spied the Jungle Cruise. My _____ (7) pleaded with Mum, Dad and myself to go on this first. We all agreed and _____ (8) aboard the small boat.

The captain was dressed in a _____ (9) safari suit. He informed the passengers about the cruise and some of the _____ (10) and experiences that lay ahead. Along the river banks were many species of _____ (11) animals. In the water, herds of hippopotamuses and buffaloes looked up at us. Flocks of jungle birds either waded in the shallows, or _____ (12) in the trees. It really felt as if we were in the jungle.

Suddenly, _____ (13) rang through the air. The captain had pretended to shoot a wild animal that had _____ (14) the boat. It was scary!

All too _____ (15) the Jungle Cruise came to an end. However, it had given us an appetite to try many more rides!

planned	express	soon	threatened	first
America	breakfast	sister	dangers	gunshots
perched	clambered	headed	brown	wild

Jungle Cruise

A trip to America would not be complete without a _____ (1) to Disneyland! My
family were awake bright and early on the _____ (2) we had planned our visit.

After breakfast we caught the courtesy _____ (3) to Disneyland. We alighted
from the bus and headed towards the huge gates. There were already several hundred
_____ (4) queuing. As Dad had bought our day passes earlier in the week, we
were able to go _____ (5) the express gate.

'Adventureland' was _____ (6) first choice. Wandering slowly through the
entrance we spied the Jungle Cruise. My sister pleaded with Mum, _____ (7) and
myself to go on this first. We all _____ (8) and clambered aboard the small boat.

The captain was _____ (9) in a brown safari suit. He informed the passengers
about the cruise and _____ (10) of the dangers and experiences that lay ahead.
Along the river banks were many _____ (11) of wild animals. In the water, herds
of hippopotamuses and buffaloes looked up at us. Flocks of jungle _____ (12)
either waded in the shallows, or perched in the trees. It really felt as if we were in the jungle.

Suddenly, gunshots rang through the air. The _____ (13) had pretended to shoot
a wild _____ (14) that had threatened the boat. It was scary!

All too soon the Jungle Cruise came to an _____ (15). However, it had given us
an appetite to try many more rides!

Gold

Gold is a precious _____ (1) that has been a sign of wealth for centuries. It can be found in veins under the Earth's surface, as large particles called _____ (2), as grains in the beds of streams or as tiny grains in _____ (3).

Gold is valuable because it is so scarce and has special _____ (4). It is easy to work with and can be hammered into _____ (5) paper sheets or drawn out into fine wire. When shaped into the desired form, it does not rust or _____ (6) in the air.

Jewellers create many beautiful _____ (7) of jewellery from gold. However, because gold is a very _____ (8) metal, it has to be combined with other metals so that it will keep its shape. This mixture is called an _____ (9). If you look closely at a piece of gold jewellery, you will see a special _____ (10) somewhere on it. This stamp tells you how much actual gold you are buying. Pure gold has the stamp 24ct (carats), which means you are buying 24 parts of _____ (11) gold. The stamp 18ct means you are buying 18 parts of pure gold and six parts of other metals.

Gold also varies in _____ (12), depending on what metals have been mixed with it.

Blue is not a colour you would think was related to gold, however, blue jeans were originally designed as a hard-wearing garment for gold prospectors. During the goldrushes of the 1800s, prospectors _____ (13) to places around the world where gold had been discovered, in the hope of getting _____ (14) quickly. Some lucky ones did, but many went home from the goldfields poorer and exhausted. Some even _____ (15).

sea water	tarnish	pieces	died	flocked
properties	metal	stamp	pure	rich
nuggets	thin	soft	alloy	colour

Gold

Gold is a precious metal that has been a _____ (1) of wealth for centuries. It can be found in veins _____ (2) the Earth's surface, as large particles _____ (3) nuggets, as grains in the beds of streams or as tiny grains in sea water.

Gold is valuable _____ (4) it is so scarce and has special properties. It is easy to work _____ (5) and can be hammered into thin paper sheets or drawn out _____ (6) fine wire. When shaped into the desired form, it does not rust or tarnish in the air.

Jewellers create many beautiful pieces of jewellery from _____ (7). However, because gold is a very soft metal, it has to be combined with _____ (8) metals so that it will keep its shape. This mixture is called an alloy. If you _____ (9) closely at a piece of gold jewellery, you will see a special _____ (10) somewhere on it. This stamp tells you how much actual gold you are buying. Pure gold has the stamp 24ct (carats), which means you are _____ (11) 24 parts of pure gold. The stamp 18ct means you are buying 18 parts of pure gold and six parts of other metals.

Gold also varies in colour, depending on what metals _____ (12) been mixed with it.

Blue is not a colour you would think was related to gold, however, blue jeans were originally designed as a hard-wearing garment for gold prospectors. _____ (13) the goldrushes of the 1800s, prospectors flocked to places around the _____ (14) where gold had been discovered, in the hope of _____ (15) rich quickly. Some lucky ones did, but many went home from the goldfields poorer and exhausted. Some even died.

Turtles

Turtles are the only _____ (1) that have a shell. These vary in colour from plain black, brown or dark green to _____ (2) green, orange, red or yellow markings. The shell provides protection like a suit of _____ (3). When in danger, most species of turtle can pull their head, legs and _____ (4) into their shell.

There are about _____ (5) species of turtles living today. Some live in the sea, some in fresh water and others live on land near _____ (6). A turtle that lives on land is called a tortoise.

As turtles are _____ (7) animals, those that live in areas with cold winters need to hibernate. Freshwater turtles _____ (8) into the warm, muddy bottom of a pond or stream to sleep. Land turtles bury themselves in soil or under _____ (9) vegetation.

All turtles lay their eggs on land. The _____ (10) turtle digs a hole in the ground, lays her eggs and covers them. The _____ (11) of the sun hatches the eggs. The baby turtles then _____ (12) their way to the surface and make their way toward the water. Many animals _____ (13) on the newborn turtles at this time.

Many kinds of turtles are endangered because humans have used turtles for food and their shells for _____ (14). Pollution and destruction of their natural habitats have _____ (15) endangered the turtle. Zoologists and scientist have set up turtle farms in certain areas to study and protect rare species.

armour	water	cold-blooded	female	tail
bright	reptiles	warmth	further	dig
prey	burrow	250	rotting	ornaments

Turtles

Turtles are the _____ (1) reptiles that have a shell. These vary in _____ (2) from plain black, brown or dark green to bright green, orange, red or yellow markings. The shell provides protection _____ (3) a suit of armour. When in danger, most species of turtle can pull their head, legs and tail into their _____ (4).

There are about 250 species of turtles living today. Some _____ (5) in the sea, some in fresh water and others live on land near water. A _____ (6) that lives on land is called a tortoise.

As turtles are cold-blooded animals, those that live in _____ (7) with cold winters need to hibernate. Freshwater turtles burrow into the warm, muddy bottom of a pond or stream _____ (8) sleep. Land turtles bury themselves in soil or _____ (9) rotting vegetation.

All turtles lay their _____ (10) on land. The female turtle digs a hole in the ground, _____ (11) her eggs and covers them. The warmth of the sun _____ (12) the eggs. The baby turtles then dig their way to the surface and make their way toward the water. Many animals prey on the _____ (13) turtles at this time.

Many _____ (14) of turtles are endangered because humans have used turtles for food and their shells for ornaments. Pollution and destruction of _____ (15) natural habitats have further endangered the turtle. Zoologists and scientist have set up turtle farms in certain areas to study and protect rare species.

Oceanarium

Visiting an oceanarium is a fascinating _____ (1). I thoroughly enjoyed

my tour of an oceanarium and observing the most _____ (2) array of sea

creatures.

My first stop was a tank with an enormous _____ (3) staring at me with

unblinking eyes. I moved along to the octopus tank and watched its _____ (4)

move in impossible directions with hundreds of _____ (5) on each.

Next was the piranha _____ (6). They looked beautiful, with _____ (7)

highlights glistening on their skin. Could these be the flesh-eating fish from South

_____ (8)? They looked more like overgrown goldfish.

I moved on and down some stairs into a huge _____ (9) tunnel, with a conveyor

_____ (10) pathway running down the middle. A multitude of fish and a large variety of

other _____ (11) creatures floated overhead and to the sides.

As I turned one _____ (12), things became darker and spookier. Moray _____ (13)

peered out at me from holes in the rocks. Further along was the shark tank. These

_____ (14) of the ocean swam around serenely with huge stingrays.

Finally, I _____ (15) from the tunnel, captivated by the underwater world I had

witnessed.

amazing	tentacles	tank	perspex	eels
suckers	silver	emerged	predators	corner
experience	ocean	belt	America	crayfish

Oceanarium

Visiting an oceanarium is a fascinating experience. I thoroughly _____ (1) my

tour of an oceanarium and observing the most amazing array of _____ (2)

creatures.

My first stop was a tank with an enormous crayfish staring at me with unblinking

_____ (3). I moved along to the octopus tank and _____ (4) its

tentacles move in impossible directions with hundreds of suckers on _____ (5).

Next was the piranha tank. They _____ (6) beautiful, with silver highlights

glistening on their skin. Could these be the flesh-eating fish _____ (7) South

America? _____ (8) looked more like overgrown goldfish.

I moved on and down _____ (9) stairs into a huge perspex tunnel, with a

conveyor belt pathway running down the _____ (10). A multitude of

_____ (11) and a large variety of other ocean creatures floated overhead and to

the sides.

As I turned one corner, things _____ (12) darker and spookier. Moray eels peered

out at me from holes in the rocks. Further _____ (13) was the shark tank. These

predators of the ocean swam around serenely _____ (14) huge stingrays.

Finally, I emerged from the tunnel, captivated by the _____ (15) world I had

witnessed.

Diamonds

Diamonds have been prized throughout _____ (1) for their beauty and durability.

They are the _____ (2), naturally-occurring substance in the world.

Diamonds are crystals made almost entirely from _____ (3) that has been under

great pressure and _____ (4). While most have eight faces, some diamond crystals have

_____ (5) and others may have very complex shapes.

A diamond can only be cut by another _____ (6). It can be split, however, by a

heavy blow due to its 'cleavage'. This is a property that enables it to split in certain directions

and produce a _____ (7), even surface.

Natural diamonds can be found in deposits along riverbeds or in

_____ (8) called kimberlite which form pipe-shaped bodies.

In many parts of the world a diamond is the

_____ (9) jewel for an engagement

ring. Gem diamonds are cut in a special way to

show their _____ (10) brilliance. The

better the stone is cut, the more

_____ (11) it has.

Diamonds _____ (12) for

gemstones are used in industry to cut, grind

and _____ (13) very hard metal with

_____ (14) and accuracy. Synthetic

diamonds are now being used in

_____ (15) as the supply of

natural diamonds cannot meet the demand.

carbon	flat	diamond	rocks	value
colour	unsuitable	industry	hardest	history
heat	traditional	bore	speed	six

Diamonds

Diamonds have been prized throughout history for their beauty _____ (1)

durability. They are the hardest, naturally-occurring substance in the _____ (2).

Diamonds are crystals _____ (3) almost entirely from carbon that has

_____ (4) under great pressure and heat. While most have eight faces, some

diamond crystals have six and _____ (5) may have very complex shapes.

A diamond can only be cut by _____ (6) diamond. It can be split, however,

_____ (7) a heavy blow due to its 'cleavage'. This is a property that enables it to

split in certain directions and produce a flat, even surface.

Natural diamonds can be _____ (8) in deposits along riverbeds or in rocks called

kimberlite which form pipe-shaped bodies.

In many parts of the world a _____ (9) is the traditional _____ (10) for

an engagement ring. Gem diamonds are cut in a special way to show their colour brilliance.

The better the stone is cut, the _____ (11) value it has.

Diamonds unsuitable for gemstones are _____ (12) in industry to cut, grind and

bore very hard metal _____ (13) speed and accuracy. Synthetic diamonds are

now being used in industry as the supply of _____ (14) diamonds cannot meet the

_____ (15).

Computers

A computer is a machine that can perform calculations and process _____ (1) according to a series of stored instructions called a _____ (2). They are designed to make tasks _____ (3) and quicker to complete.

Computers vary in size, _____ (4) and ability according to the type and number of _____ (5) it needs to do. Although the first computers in the 1960s were as big as a _____ (6), they could not perform the tasks of a modern desktop computer.

Computers are used extensively in industry, education, _____ (7) and office administration. They are also becoming increasingly popular for _____ (8) use.

Information can be stored on _____ (9) disc, CD or on the computer's hard drive. Microphones, speakers, _____ (10), CD Roms and modems can be added to further enhance a computer's capabilities. A _____ (11) linked to a computer enables work to be reproduced. Commonly used printers _____ (12) the dot matrix, ink jet and laser.

Computer-controlled _____ (13) can be used to perform repetitive jobs with speed and _____ (14). In our society computers are being used to perform more and more tasks, but the most _____ (15) computer of all is still the human brain.

easier	classroom	include	printer	complex
information	jobs	home	research	accuracy
robots	floppy	speed	scanners	program

Computers

A computer is a _____ [1] that can perform calculations and process information according to a series of stored instructions _____ [2] a program. They are designed to make _____ [3] easier and quicker to complete.

Computers _____ [4] in size, speed and ability according to the type and number of jobs it _____ [5] to do. Although the first computers in the 1960s were as big as a classroom, they _____ [6] not perform the tasks of a modern desktop computer.

Computers are _____ [7] extensively in industry, education, research and office administration. They are _____ [8] becoming increasingly popular for home use.

Information can be stored on floppy _____ [9], CD or on the computer's hard drive. Microphones, speakers, scanners, CD Roms _____ [10] modems can be added to further enhance a computer's capabilities. A printer linked to a _____ [11] enables work to be reproduced. Commonly used printers include _____ [12] dot matrix, ink jet and laser.

Computer-controlled robots can be used to _____ [13] repetitive jobs with speed and accuracy. In our society computers are being used to perform _____ [14] and more tasks, but the most complex computer of all is _____ [15] the human brain.

Back to Ancient Egypt

My friend and I had an _____ (1) adventure yesterday. Tom
and I had learnt about _____ (2) Egypt in school and we were
trying to imagine what it would be like to have lived there. We must have
powerful imaginations because _____ (3) we found
ourselves standing on the lush banks of the _____ (4) River .

Surrounding us were crops of wheat and _____ (5). An ingenious
irrigation system of canals carried _____ (6) from the Nile to the
crops. It was so hot that it was hard to imagine how _____ (7)
could grow.

The men wore white _____ (8) wraps and the _____ (9) long,
tight white dresses. Some people wore sandals, make-up and headdresses.
We thought they must be _____ (10) to trade for things other than food.
We had learnt in class that the Egyptians didn't have money and
_____ (11) excess items for those they needed.

The people didn't seem to rush about, they worked
_____ (12) yet looked relaxed - not like the
people of today. When the work was done,
many of the families went down to the river to
_____ (13) or sail their boats which
appeared to be made of papyrus reeds.

Seeing the families together made us
_____ (14) of our own. We
found ourselves back in our own time
again. Next time we'd like to visit the
_____ (15)!

ancient	Nile	suddenly	anything	fish
pyramids	think	hard	rich	traded
women	skirt	incredible	barley	water

Back to Ancient Egypt

My friend and I had an incredible adventure yesterday. Tom and _____ (1) had learnt about ancient _____ (2) in school and we were trying to imagine what it would be like to have _____ (3) there. We must have powerful imaginations because suddenly we found ourselves standing on the lush banks of the _____ (4) Nile.

Surrounding us were _____ (5) of wheat and barley. An ingenious irrigation system of canals carried water from the _____ (6) to the crops. It was so hot that it was hard to imagine how anything could _____ (7).

The men _____ (8) white skirt wraps and the women long, tight white dresses. _____ (9) people wore sandals, make-up and headdresses. We thought they _____ (10) be rich to trade for things other than food. We had learnt in _____ (11) that the Egyptians didn't have money and traded excess items for those they needed.

The people didn't seem to rush about, they _____ (12) hard yet looked relaxed - not like the people of today. When the work was done, many of the families went down to the river to fish or sail their _____ (13) which appeared to be made of papyrus reeds.

Seeing the families together made us think of _____ (14) own. We found ourselves back in our own time again. Next time we'd like to _____ (15) the pyramids!

The Great Wall of China

The Great Wall of China is the _____ (1) structure ever built. It stretches from the _____ (2) coast to north-central China and is almost 6,400 kilometres in length. The wall follows a _____ (3) course that crosses over mountains and hills and along the borders of _____ (4).

Construction of the wall began more than _____ (5) years ago. China once had many separate kingdoms who made their own walls to keep out _____ (6). When China became unified all the walls were linked together and _____ (7).

The effort required _____ (8) of thousands of workers as it was constructed entirely by hand. Much of the wall has sides made of _____ (9) or bricks. The inside of the wall was filled with _____ (10) and the top was paved with bricks set in mortar. The bricks formed a road which could be used to transport soldiers, _____ (11) and equipment. Watchtowers were built about 150 _____ (12) apart along the wall.

The wall was successful in protecting China from _____ (13) attacks but was ineffective against a _____ (14) invasion. Through the centuries much of the wall has collapsed. Parts have been restored as it has become China's _____ (15) tourist attraction.

greatest	hundreds	2,000	longest	winding
invaders	minor	stone	metres	extended
eastern	horses	major	earth	deserts

The Great Wall of China

The _____ (1) Wall of China is the longest structure ever _____ (2). It stretches from the eastern coast to north-central China and is almost 6,400 kilometres in _____ (3). The wall follows a winding course that crosses _____ (4) mountains and hills and along the borders of deserts.

Construction of the wall began more than 2,000 _____ (5) ago. _____ (6) once had many separate kingdoms who made their _____ (7) walls to keep out invaders. When China became unified _____ (8) the walls were linked together and extended.

The effort required hundreds of thousands of _____ (9) as it was constructed entirely by hand. Much of the wall has sides _____ (10) of stone or bricks. The inside of the wall was filled _____ (11) earth and the top was paved with bricks set in mortar. The bricks formed a road which could be used to _____ (12) soldiers, horses and equipment. Watchtowers were built about 150 metres apart _____ (13) the wall.

The _____ (14) was successful in protecting China from minor attacks but was ineffective against a major invasion. Through the centuries much of the wall has collapsed. Parts have been restored as it has become China's greatest tourist _____ (15).

The Mystery of Magic

Magician, _____ (1) and illusionist are all names for people who perform magic tricks. Audiences are fascinated by the seemingly impossible feats these entertainers can _____ (2).

People enjoy magic because of its _____ (3). The _____ (4) of how a trick is done will make it lose its appeal. Magicians _____ (5) reveal the secrets of their tricks.

Magic includes many types of _____ (6). Sleight of hand is when objects such as balls, cards or _____ (7) are made to appear and disappear. Illusions involve large-scale tricks with the aid of human assistants and elaborate _____ (8). One of the most famous illusions is _____ (9) a person in half!

Some magicians specialise in _____ (10) magic. The most _____ (11) escape performer was Harry Houdini who could quickly free himself from handcuffs, leg irons, jail cells and nailed _____ (12). His most sensational feat was to escape from an airtight tank filled with _____ (13)!

Simple _____ (14) tricks can be learned from books on magic. To become a professional _____ (15), however, takes many years of practice.

achieve	tricks	famous	magician	water
conjurer	mystery	equipment	escape	magic
crates	discovery	doves	sawing	seldom

The Mystery of Magic

Magician, conjurer and illusionist are all _____ (1) for people who perform magic tricks. Audiences are fascinated by the seemingly impossible feats _____ (2) entertainers can achieve.

People enjoy _____ (3) because of its mystery. The discovery of how a _____ (4) is done will make it lose its appeal. Magicians seldom reveal the secrets of _____ (5) tricks.

Magic includes many types of tricks. Sleight of hand is when objects _____ (6) as balls, cards or doves are made to _____ (7) and disappear. Illusions involve large-scale tricks with the _____ (8) of human assistants and elaborate equipment. One of the most famous illusions is sawing a person in _____ (9)!

Some _____ (10) specialise in escape magic. The most famous escape performer _____ (11) Harry Houdini who could quickly free himself from handcuffs, leg irons, jail _____ (12) and nailed crates. His most sensational feat was to escape from an airtight tank _____ (13) with water!

Simple magic tricks can be learned from _____ (14) on magic. To become a professional magician, however, takes _____ (15) years of practice.

Family Reunion

A _____ (1) of fog covered the land below with only patches of green grass and some large _____ (2) visible.

Melanie and her mother were a little apprehensive as _____ (3) plane descended through the fog and were relieved when they _____ (4) landed. Quickly retrieving their _____ (5), they walked towards the customs queue. After passing through customs they headed for the arrival _____ (6) of the airport.

Their eyes scanned the many _____ (7) that were eagerly awaiting the arrival of _____ (8) and family. Melanie had only _____ (9) recollections of her uncle, but her mother instantly recognised her brother-in-law in the _____ (10). She quickly ran towards the tall, _____ (11) man and they embraced each other warmly. Melanie, rather shyly, gave him a hug.

Melanie's _____ (12) was waiting impatiently at home. As they pulled into the driveway she came _____ (13) out to meet them. Hugging and kissing each other, laughing and _____ (14) they entered the house. Melanie was looking forward to listening to all the memories that would be shared during their visit. What a _____ (15) reunion!

their	faces	thin	aunty	happy
blanket	friends	crowd	rushing	buildings
finally	area	luggage	vague	crying

Family Reunion

A blanket of fog covered the _____ (1) below with only patches of green

_____ (2) and some large buildings visible.

Melanie and her mother were a little apprehensive as their _____ (3) descended

through the fog and were relieved when they finally _____ (4). Quickly

retrieving their luggage, they walked _____ (5) the customs queue. After passing

through customs _____ (6) headed for the arrival area of the airport.

Their _____ (7) scanned the many faces that were eagerly awaiting the

_____ (8) of friends and family.

Melanie had only vague

recollections of

_____ (9) uncle,

but her mother instantly

recognised her brother-in-law

in the crowd. She quickly ran

towards the tall, thin

_____ (10) and

they embraced each other

warmly. Melanie, rather

shyly, gave him a

_____ (11).

_____ (12) aunty was waiting impatiently at home. As they pulled into the

driveway she came rushing out to _____ (13) them. Hugging and kissing each

other, laughing and crying they _____ (14) the house. Melanie was looking

forward to listening to all the memories that would be shared during their _____ (15).

What a happy reunion!

Answers

The answers provided for the second page of each topic are suggestions only. Children may select words which have not been listed but may still be correct if their answer is used in context.

Page 1 - Dolphins

1. wave 2. sociable 3. people 4. body 5. smallest
6. dorsal 7. smooth 8. warm 9. trained 10. each
11. moans 12. dolphins 13. oil 14. Conservationists
15. observe

Page 2 - Dolphins

1. boat/ship 2. are 3. around/with 4. its 5. have 6. a
7. water/sea/air 8. keeps 9. Dolphins/They 10. in 11. of
12. for 13. fish 14. to 15. and

Page 3 - Rugby

1. team 2. Britain 3. fifteen 4. eight 5. specific 6. chase
7. metre 8. win 9. penalty 10. try 11. tackle 12. country
13. uniform 14. national 15. African

Page 4 - Rugby

1. world 2. sport 3. with 4. team 5. has 6. of 7. ball
8. across/over 9. game 10. and/or 11. allowed/able
12. rugby 13. wear 14. called 15. New

Page 5 - Jungle Cruise

1. America 2. planned 3. breakfast 4. headed 5. express
6. first 7. sister 8. clambered 9. brown 10. dangers
11. wild 12. perched 13. gunshots 14. threatened
15. soon

Page 6 - Jungle Cruise

1. visit/trip 2. day/morning 3. bus 4. people/visitors/tourists
5. through 6. our 7. Dad 8. agreed 9. dressed 10. some/
warned/many 11. species/types/kinds 12. birds 13. captain
14. animal 15. end

Page 7 - Gold

1. metal 2. nuggets 3. sea water 4. properties 5. thin
6. tarnish 7. pieces 8. soft 9. alloy 10. stamp 11. pure
12. colour 13. flocked 14. rich 15. died

Page 8 - Gold

1. sign/source 2. under/below/in 3. called 4. because/as
5. with 6. into 7. gold 8. other 9. look 10. stamp
11. buying/purchasing 12. have 13. During/In 14. world
15. getting/becoming

Page 9 - Turtles

1. reptiles 2. bright 3. armour 4. tail 5. 250 6. water
7. cold-blooded 8. burrow 9. rotting 10. female
11. warmth 12. dig 13. prey 14. ornaments 15. further

Page 10 - Turtles

1. only 2. colour 3. like 4. shell 5. live 6. turtle 7. areas/
places/countries/regions 8. to 9. under/in/among 10. eggs
11. lays 12. hatches 13. newborn/baby/tiny 14. kinds/
types/species 15. their

Page 11 - Oceanarium

1. experience 2. amazing 3. crayfish 4. tentacles
5. suckers 6. tank 7. silver 8. America 9. perspex 10. belt
11. ocean 12. corner 13. eels 14. predators 15. emerged

Page 12 - Oceanarium

1. enjoyed 2. sea/ocean 3. eyes 4. watched/saw/observed/
noticed 5. each/them 6. looked/were 7. from/of 8. They
9. some/the 10. middle/centre 11. fish 12. became/
appeared 13. along/around/ahead 14. with
15. underwater/ocean

Page 13 - Diamonds

1. history 2. hardest 3. carbon 4. heat 5. six
6. diamond 7. flat 8. rocks 9. traditional 10. colour
11. value 12. unsuitable 13. bore 14. speed 15. industry

Page 14 - Diamonds

1. and 2. world 3. made 4. been 5. others/some
6. another 7. by/with 8. found/located 9. diamond
10. jewel/stone/gem 11. more 12. used 13. with
14. natural/real 15. demand

Page 15 - Computers

1. information 2. program 3. easier 4. speed 5. jobs
6. classroom 7. research 8. home 9. floppy 10. scanners
11. printer 12. include 13. robots 14. accuracy
15. complex

Page 16 - Computers

1. machine 2. called/on 3. tasks/jobs/things 4. vary/differ/
range 5. needs/has 6. could/did 7. used 8. also/now
9. disc 10. and 11. computer 12. the 13. perform/do
14. more 15. still

Page 17 - Back to Ancient Egypt

1. incredible 2. ancient 3. suddenly 4. Nile 5. barley
6. water 7. anything 8. skirt 9. women 10. rich 11. traded
12. hard 13. fish 14. think 15. pyramids

Page 18 - Back to Ancient Egypt

1. I 2. Egypt 3. lived/been 4. River 5. crops/fields 6. Nile/
river 7. grow/survive 8. wore 9. Some/the 10. must
11. class/school/history 12. worked 13. boats 14. our
15. visit

Page 19 - The Great Wall of China

1. longest 2. eastern 3. winding 4. deserts 5. 2,000
6. invaders 7. extended 8. hundreds 9. stone 10. earth
11. horses 12. metres 13. minor 14. major 15. greatest

Page 20 - The Great Wall of China

1. Great 2. built/made 3. length 4. over/many 5. years
6. China 7. own 8. all 9. workers/people 10. made
11. with 12. transport /carry 13. along 14. wall
15. attraction

Page 21 - The Mystery of Magic

1. conjurer 2. achieve 3. mystery 4. discovery 5. seldom
6. tricks 7. doves 8. equipment 9. sawing 10. escape
11. famous 12. crates 13. water 14. magic 15. magician

Page 22 - The Mystery of Magic

1. names/titles 2. these 3. magic 4. trick 5. their 6. such
7. appear 8. aid/help/use 9. half 10. magicians 11. was
12. cells 13. filled 14. books 15. many/several

Page 23 - Family Reunion

1. blanket 2. buildings 3. their 4. finally 5. luggage
6. area 7. faces 8. friends 9. vague 10. crowd 11. thin
12. aunty 13. rushing 14. crying 15. happy

Page 24 - Family Reunion

1. land/earth/city 2. grass 3. plane/aircraft 4. landed
5. towards/to 6. they 7. eyes 8. arrival 9. her 10. man
11. hug 12. Melanie's/Her 13. meet/greet 14. entered
15. visit/stay/holiday